Life is sweet in Berry Bitty City.

Dancing makes the heart smile!

A berry sweet ballerina.

Strawberry serves yummy treats.

©TCFC

Thank you, Strawberry!

Orange Blossom

Look up, down, across and diagonally.

EARTH   CARING   BLOSSOM   LUSCIOUS
FRUIT TREE   GROW   FRAGRANT   ORCHARDS

```
C D E F I C N O U S C G
O A L H C O C E S R I R
F F R U I T T R E E S O
R M A H E R G K A I L W
A O R C H A R D S B B R
G P L U S C I O U S A I
R P B L O S S O M E R G
A N K C E J K M G D N L
N C S K A S D G N I N N
T I R L R K M A R R G Y
L M S I T V E A A I S N
C E N R H L C C Z H L F
```

Orange Blossom runs the Orange Mart.

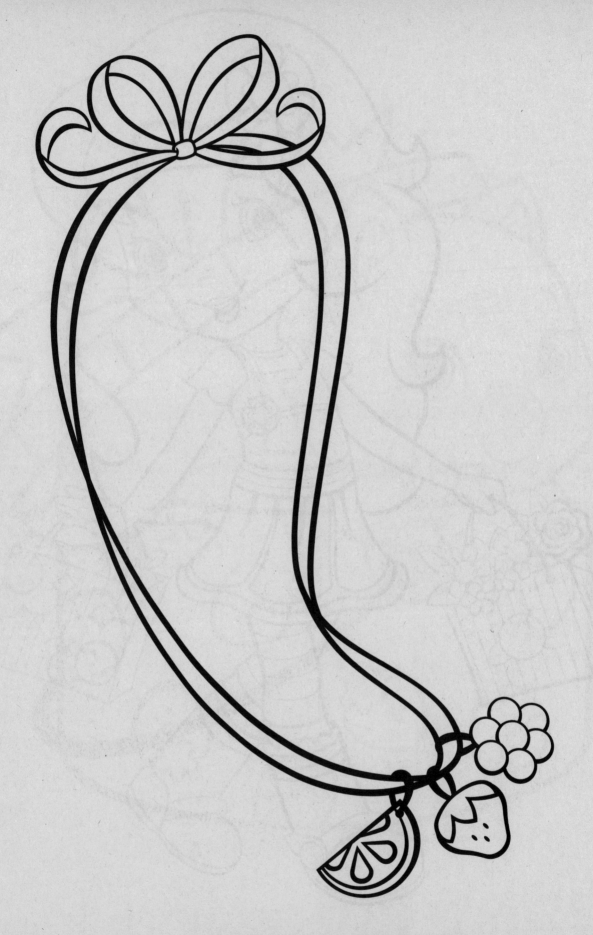

A charming necklace.

Peek-a-boo kitty!

The Berrykins harvest berries.

Which purse is different?

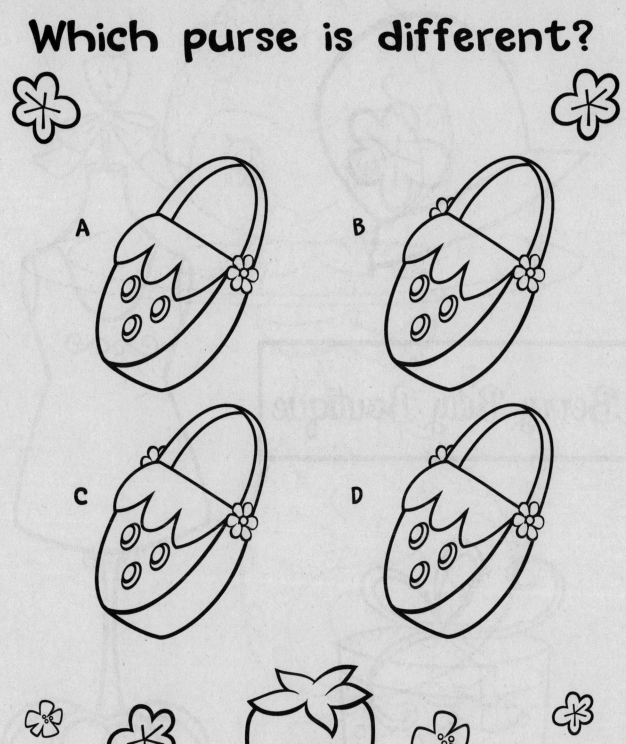

A

B

C

D

Answer:

_____

Berry Bitty Boutique

Berry Bitty City has many delightful little shops.

Custard loves Strawberry Shortcake.

Little girl. Big possibilities.

Strawberry Shortcake

Look up, down, across, and diagonally.

HEART   BERRY   SWEET   SPUNKY
SMILE   CUTIE   FRIENDS   ADVENTUROUS

```
A Y B R N S W E E T V D
O A L H C S F K B F M H
M Y D R T U J L D R C E
O Z L V N S T K M I V A
T D S M E L E I N E Q R
Z P L T Y N K R E N T T
S P U N K Y T I J D S G
B N K L Y J K U J S N O
T C E B N E V I R P T K
S M I L E J M A J O B Q
L I L W Y F K E V P U G
B E R R Y E J I B S T S
```

Blueberry Muffin runs Blueberry Books.

©TCFC

Pupcake is a sweet little friend.

Help Strawberry Shortcake get to the strawberries.

Start

Finish

Fresh off the vine!

Strawberry runs the Berry Café.

Lemon Meringue runs the Lemon Salon.

A little fun is all you need.

Which Berrykin is different?

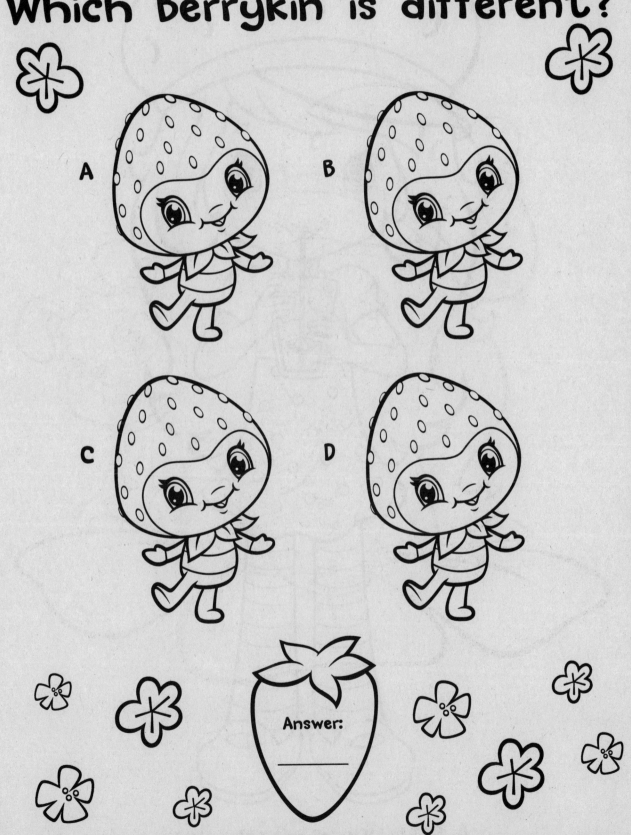

A

B

C

D

Answer:
____

Life is sweet!

So refreshing!

Which line will lead Strawberry Shortcake to her new hat?

1

2

3

Answer:

Window shopping.

Strawberry loves to shop.

Keep love in your heart.

Plum Pudding runs Sweet Beats Studio.

A twirly girl.

A little sweetness goes a long way.

How many words can you make from the letters in:

Lemon Meringue

Follow the numbers 1 to 10 to help Custard find Pupcake.

We like sweet surprises!

Strawberry is ready to shop.

Orange Blossom joins in the fun.

Fresh from the garden.

Berrykins are happy little workers.

Fresh and fruity!

Lovely and lively!

Which line leads to Pupcake?

1   2   3

Answer:

©TCFC

Strawberry loves all her friends.

Which necklace is different?

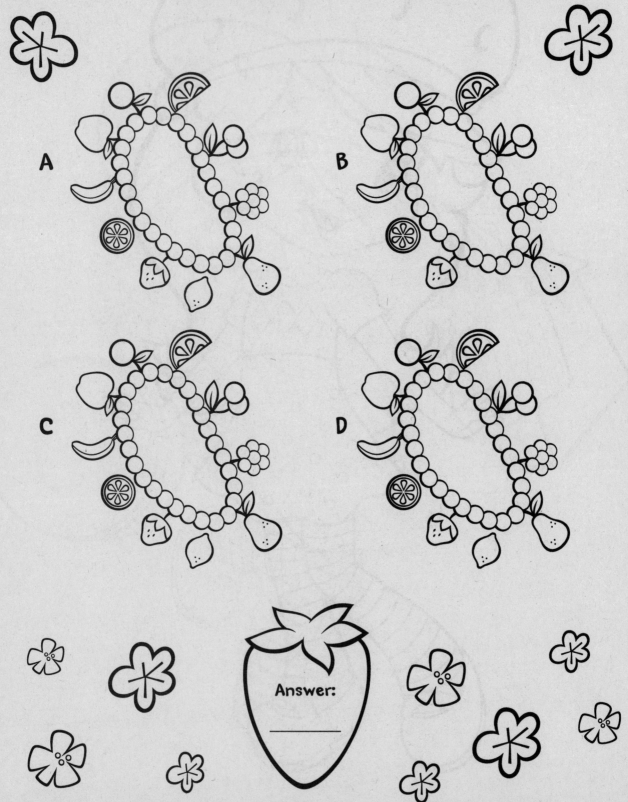

A

B

C

D

Answer:

_____

What a wonderful day!

How many words can you make from the letters in:
Orange Blossom

©TCFC

Add a pop of fruity color!

Friendship is the best gift of all.

Strawberry Shortcake lives in Berry Bitty City.

Plum Pudding is a graceful dancer.

©TCFC

Happiness adds a skip to your step.

Raspberry Torte sells berry sweet fashions.

Pretty hat boxes.

Gifts for friends.

Help Orange Blossom find her way to the flowers.

Start

Finish

Design a dress!

Yum is in the air!

Berry Bitty City is a fun place to live.

Which line leads to Strawberry Shortcake?

1

2

3

Answer:

Which Custard is different?

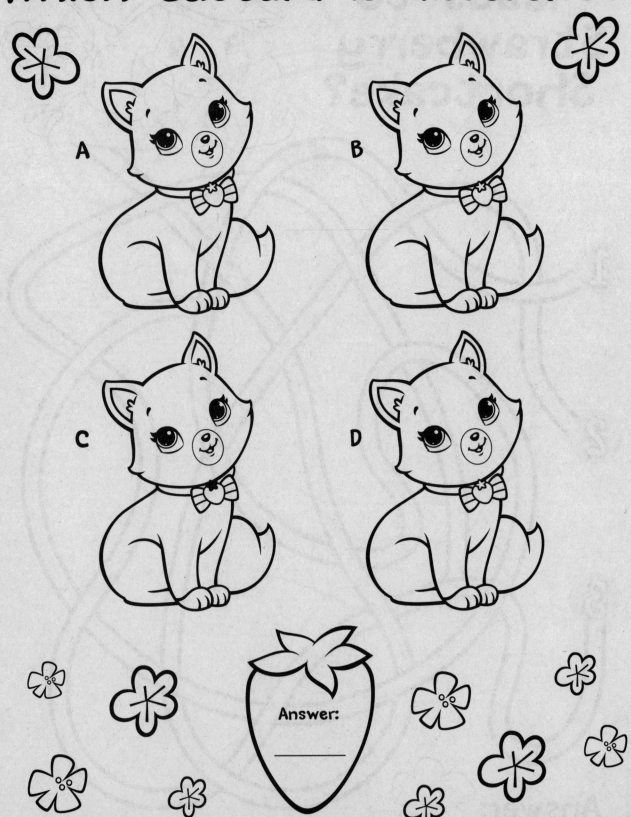

A

B

C

D

Answer:

_____

On our way to a sunshiny day!

Which line leads to Orange Blossom?

A   B   C

Answer:

Are you ready for a new style?

How many words can you make from the letters in:

Berry Special

_____   _____

_____   _____

_____   _____

_____   _____

_____

_____

_____

_____

_____

_____

_____

Berry yummy!

Raspberry Torte runs fresh fashions boutique.

Blueberry Muffin sells berry fun books.

Which line leads to Lemon Meringue?

A

B

C

Answer:

Berry Bitty
Boutique

Styles for smiles.

Time for dance class.

Tap your toes!

Pickin' and gigglin'!

THE BERRY BEST

Word Search

Look up, down, across, and diagonally
for these berry special words.

```
G K B L E A F S B
O R L B E A U T I E U L
W T E L A R S R S R G F
L C I E T S A V E R E R
O R D C N A K I A Y E U
V E H U S D S E R B G I
R L S E E D S Z T S K T
    R L E F T U I M N
    D T B B T B R V
    J A M A T U E I
    P A T C H R N
    I Y L S E O E
```

VINE	LEAF	PATCH
RED	JAM	FRUIT
SEEDS	BERRY	BASKET

Custard is a cuddle cat.

Love makes the flowers grow.

How many words can you make from the letters in:
Blueberry Muffin

_____   _____

_____   _____

_____   _____

_____   _____

_____   _____

_____   _____

_____   _____

_____

Let's design an outfit!

Full of sunny sweetness!

Tutti-frutti cuties!

Let's meet at the Berry Café!

Which hat box is different?

A

B

C

D

Answer:

_____

Life is Delicious!

Look up, down, across, and diagonally
for these berry special words.

```
D L N G S F R O S T I N G D
E Q O C I C E C R E A M Q T
G R R L S T V A N I L L A R
S G B N L G E D E S S E R T
C C O O K I E S I C R G O V
W W I L T D P B B T B N W Y
Q Q S C H O C O L A T E Q U
S C H E W Y I N P O U D S M
```

DESSERT

TREAT

CHEWY

LOLLIPOP

CHOCOLATE

ICE CREAM

YUM

FROSTING

COOKIES

VANILLA

Little Berry Girl

Open the door to possibilities!

Help Strawberry Shortcake find her way to the Berry Bitty Boutique.

Finish

Start

Raspberry Torte is ready for the day.

Lemon Meringue has style.

Friends are Sweet!

How many words can you make from the letters in:

Strawberry Shortcake

_____   _____

_____   _____

_____   _____

_____   _____

_____   _____

_____   _____

_____   _____

_____   _____

_____   _____

Which hat is different?

Answer:

_____

Which line will lead Strawberry Shortcake to the Berrykins?

1 2 3

Answer:

ANSWER: 1

Treat yourself to a new hair-do!

Step to the beat!

Come back soon!